Contents

Teacher Pages

Introduction

Make learning fun with the special day activities in *Dinosaur Days*! Children will enjoy using the dinosaur (tyrannosaurus, pteranodon, triceratops, brontosaurus) theme patterns as they practice readiness skills and learn science concepts.

Dinosaur Days contains 38 pages of patterns and seven teacher pages of assembly and programming suggestions. Activities cover language arts, math, and science. You'll find shape books, puppets, flash cards, pockets, money, counters, party patterns, a gameboard, and a calendar.

Dinosaur Language Arts

Dinosaur Shape Books

Use the dinosaur shape patterns (pages 11-12) for student-made booklets. Provide children with crayons, scissors, and pencils to practice writing their names, or the alphabet. Children may want to color and decorate shape book covers. Punch a hole at the tail on each page and cover, and insert a brass fastener to make a booklet of each student's work.

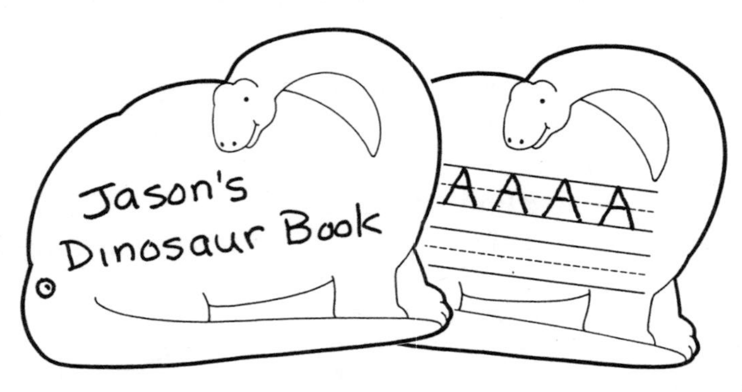

Theater and Puppets

Barn Theater and Square Dancing Puppets
for Storybook Productions

Puppets help children understand the concepts of left and right, and up and down. Use the patterns (pages 13-16) to stage a barnyard hoedown puppet show.

Provide children with the barn theater patterns (pages 13-14) and the stick puppets (pages 15-16) for their own dinosaur theater production. Supply crayons, scissors, glue, and plastic straws for students to complete their puppets. Or give children finger puppets (page 17) and tape for assembly.

Dinosaur Books

- *Count-a-Saurus* by Nancy Blumenthal
- *Dinosaur Babies* by Maida Silverman
- *Dinosaur Dream* by Dennis Nolan
- *Dinosaurs and More Dinosaurs* by M. Jean Craig
- *Dinosaurs are Different* by Aliki
- *The Story of Dinosaurs* by David Eastman

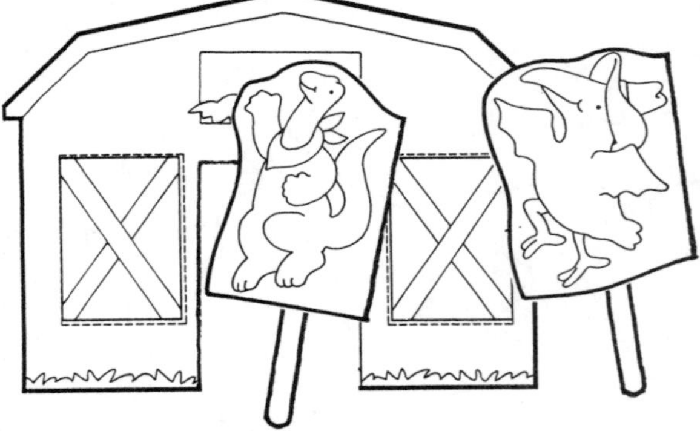

Skills Practice Worksheets Program the cut-and-paste open worksheets (pages 18-19) with a matching activity. Upper and lower case matching is perfect for these pages.

Reproduce the manuscript worksheet (page 20) for students to practice writing the alphabet. To program, write a letter or letters on the first manuscript line. Use this page as a master and make copies for each child.

Dinosaur Days

Publisher: Roberta Suid
Copy Editor: Annalisa Suid
Design and Production: Marilynn G. Barr
Cover Design: David Hale
Educational Consultant: Lillian Lieberman

For a complete catalog, write to the address above.

ISBN 1-878279-56-4

Printed in the United States of America

9 8 7 6 5 4 3 2

Teacher Pages

Dinosaur Science

Dinosaur Habitat

Baby Dinosaur Eggs

Fascinate children with facts from *Dinosaur Babies* by Maida Silverman. Encourage your students to bring toy dinosaurs to school to include in a fun-filled discussion on dinosaurs and their habitats. Then help your students make a Dinosaur Egg Collage.

Create the collage with colored tissue paper scraps and the patterns (pages 21-22).

Have children glue layers of colored tissue paper onto the egg and color the foliage green. Help children cut out the center of the egg, and glue the pattern to a sheet of construction paper. Provide each student with his or her choice of the baby dinosaurs (page 22) to color, cut out, and paste in the center of their eggs.

Discuss how the dinosaur babies differ from each other. Explain the difference between plant-eaters (brontosaurus and triceratops), meat-eaters (tyrannosaurus), and fish-eaters (pteranodon). Encourage students to pretend they are dinosaurs. Children can take turns describing where they live and what they eat. Then provide a healthy plant-eater treat for the class—celery sticks with cream cheese.

Dr. Dinosaur's Body Chart

Use the chart and body parts patterns (pages 23-24) for a unit on the body. Provide each child with a blank chart to color, cut out, and glue onto the front of a folder. After discussing different parts of the body with the class, give each child a chart, the body parts, and labels to glue onto a chart. Have children place their finished charts in their folders to display at an open house.

Reproduce the adjacent Doctor Dinosaur button for each child in the class. Provide children with the body pattern (page 24) to color and cut out. Write each child's name on the back and mount them on a "Healthy Bodies" bulletin board.

Teacher Pages

Dinosaur Math

Dinner for Two Center

A Math Skills Practice Activity

Here is an open math skills practice center for individual or group matching. Reproduce, color, cut out, and assemble the patterns (pages 26-27). Reproduce and program the sandwich patterns (page 28) on white or brown construction paper with number set dots (from 1-10). Laminate the center and pieces. Attach magnetic tape or Velcro to the center (where indicated) and to the back of each sandwich. Color, cut out, and laminate the plate patterns. Program each plate with a numeral using an erasable or wipe-off marker. Attach the plates to the center with magnetic tape or Velcro. Mount the center to the back of a decorated shoebox.

Have children sit in a circle while you hold the Dinner for Two Center in your lap. Invite children, in turn, to come up and find a matching number set sandwich to attach to each dinosaur's paw. Ask the children to count the dots out loud. Change the numeral for each child's turn.

Dino Dollars and Counter Dinosaurs

Introduce your students to counting and money concepts with the Dino Dollars and coins (page 29) and the Counters (page 25). For a shopping experience, create a "Real Deal Car Sales" display on your bulletin board. Reproduce several copies of vehicles (pages 30-33). Write the cost of the vehicles on the back, and place them in construction paper pockets for students to purchase. Provide children with dollars and coins.

Use the Counter Dinosaurs for counting practice, as decorations on student-made construction paper greeting cards, as sticker awards, or for achievement award pendants (glue to construction paper circles and lace with yarn).

Teacher Pages

Basic Dinosaurs

Dinosaur Flash Cards Reinforce color names with these delightful characters. Reproduce the Dinosaur Flash Cards (pages 38-39) for students to color with primary and secondary colors for a recognition practice activity—red, yellow, blue, green, orange, purple. Teach students how to play *Memory,* or *Go Fish.*

Program the cards with shapes for an alternate recognition activity.

Provide each child with one of the Dinosaur Pockets (pages 40-41) for card storage.

Alphabet Collage Reproduce and program the bone cards (page 46) with upper and lower case letters for each student. Provide each child with crayons, scissors, glue, and a large sheet of construction paper. Show children how to arrange and glue the bones onto their papers. Help each child write his or her name at the bottom of the page, and display the finished collages on a "Dinosaur Bones" bulletin board.

Stone Jumping Create a "Stone Jumping" gameboard along the bottom of your bulletin board. Program bone cards (page 46) with number sets from 1-10. Place the cards in a paper plate pocket and attach to the board. Mount 20 paper plates (representing stones) on the board (face down). Label the last plate "finish." Color and cut out transportation dinosaurs (pages 30-33) for children to use as pawns. Attach magnetic tape or Velcro strips to the backs of the dinosaurs and onto each stone.

To play, invite each child, in turn, to draw a card and count the dots. Then have the child move his or her dinosaur pawn the same number of stones. Play continues until a student reaches "finish."

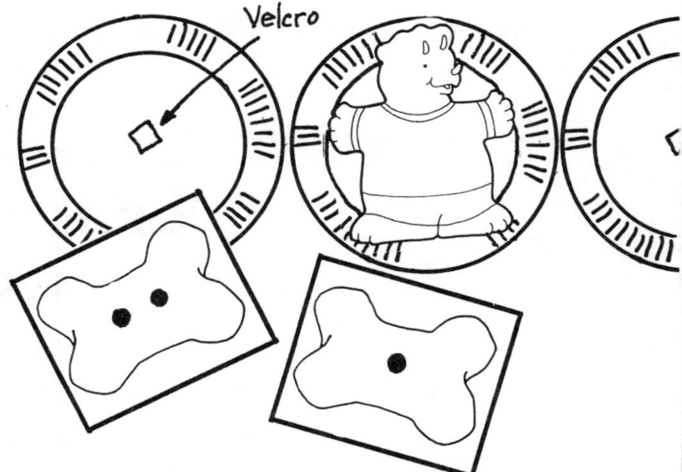

Dinosaur Pockets

Paper plates make handy storage containers. Provide each child with $1\frac{1}{2}$ paper plates and their choice of the Dinosaur Pockets (pages 40-41). Have each child color, cut out, and paste his or her dinosaur to the top of one paper plate. Staple the half plate to the front of the whole one, and then fasten these pockets to the bottom of your classroom bulletin board for children to store crayons and other craft supplies.

For a shapes sorting activity, assemble three Dinosaur Pockets—one for squares, one for triangles, and one for circles. Program the Dinosaur Flash Cards (pages 38-39) with matching shapes for students to sort into the correct pockets.

Teacher Pages

Dinosaur Day Bulletin and Flannel Board Displays

Transportation Dinosaurs

Introduce your students to traffic safety with the land, water, air, and play vehicles (pages 30-33).

Provide children with the dinosaurs, sheets of black construction paper, thin yellow construction paper strips, crayons, scissors, and glue. Have children create a street by gluing a yellow construction paper strip in the center of the black construction paper. Show how to assemble and glue the patterns onto the construction paper streets to display on a traffic safety bulletin board. To make flannel board patterns, transfer the patterns to flannel. Display the patterns on a flannel board for a rainy day class activity.

Worker Dinosaurs

Dress up your classroom bulletin board with the worker dinosaurs and matching tools (pages 34-37).

Reproduce and provide the patterns for each child to color, cut out, and glue onto construction paper. Help children write their names on their pictures. For a border, make several copies of the tools (pages 35 and 37). Color, cut out, and glue the patterns onto crepe paper or construction paper strips to span the length and width of your board. Display worker pictures on the bulletin board.

Teacher Pages

Dinonsaur Games

Dinosaur Alley

Provide students with crayons, scissors, and glue to assemble the pawns, cards, and gameboard (pages 44-46) for color recognition practice. Fill in each space on the spinner and the gameboard spaces with a different color (red, orange, yellow, green, blue, purple, brown, and black). To play, each child takes a turn spinning and moves to the next matching color space. Play continues until a student reaches the end of Dinosaur Alley.

Dinosaur Calendar

Reproduce the Dinosaur Calendar (pages 42-43) to record classroom events. Or provide each child with his or her own calendar to chart the weather, special activities, birthdays, and other important occasions.

SUNDAY	MONDAY	TUESDAY	WEDNESDAY	THURSDAY	FRIDAY	SATURDAY

Dinosaur Bonuses

Dinosaur Buddies

Reproduce these cut-out badges for student team spirit, good work, or good behavior awards. Provide students with crayons and scissors.

The Spotlight is on You! Provide each child with a flashlight pattern (page 35) to color and cut out. Write each child's name on his or her flashlight. Reproduce the open worksheet (page 20) for children to practice writing letters of the alphabet. Attach flashlights and display finished work on a "The Spotlight is on You!" bulletin board.

Dinosaur Headbands Provide each child with a pocket pattern (pages 40-41) to color and cut and a long oaktag strip to make dinosaur headbands. Have children color oaktag strips and show them how to attach dinosaurs. Measure, and secure headbands with tape.

Dinosaur Chains Reproduce the dinosaur finger puppets (page 17) for children to color and cut out. Punch a hole in each tab. Lace the dinosaurs with yarn or ribbon, and fasten the dinosaur chain to your bulletin board or windows.

Open House Displays Use the barn pattern (page 13) to decorate your bulletin board or student desks for open house. Have children color and cut out the barn. Cut a slit around the door and glue to a sheet of construction paper. Have children draw self-portraits on index cards. Glue cards inside the theater doors. Write children's names on the loft windows.

Teacher Pages

Dinosaur Parties

Party Favors, Bow Tie, and Name Tag

Make birthdays or any special events even more fun with the party patterns (page 47).

Ask parent volunteers to help the class prepare for a Dinosaur Day Party. Provide each student with a hat, straw-topper, and name tag pattern. Have children color, cut out, and assemble the party decorations for a really fun Dinosaur Day celebration!

To assemble the party hat (page 48), apply glue to the tab, roll the pattern (overlapping the tab), and secure.

For birthday students, reproduce and assemble a dinosaur bow-tie to wear on their special day.

Name Tag

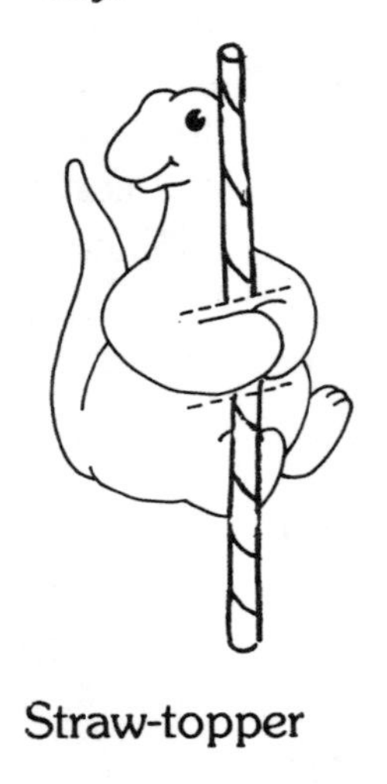

Straw-topper

Straw-topper

Color and cut out. Slit along the dotted lines and insert a straw. Tape to secure. Substitute a pencil for an incentive or recognition award for good work or behavior.

Shape Book

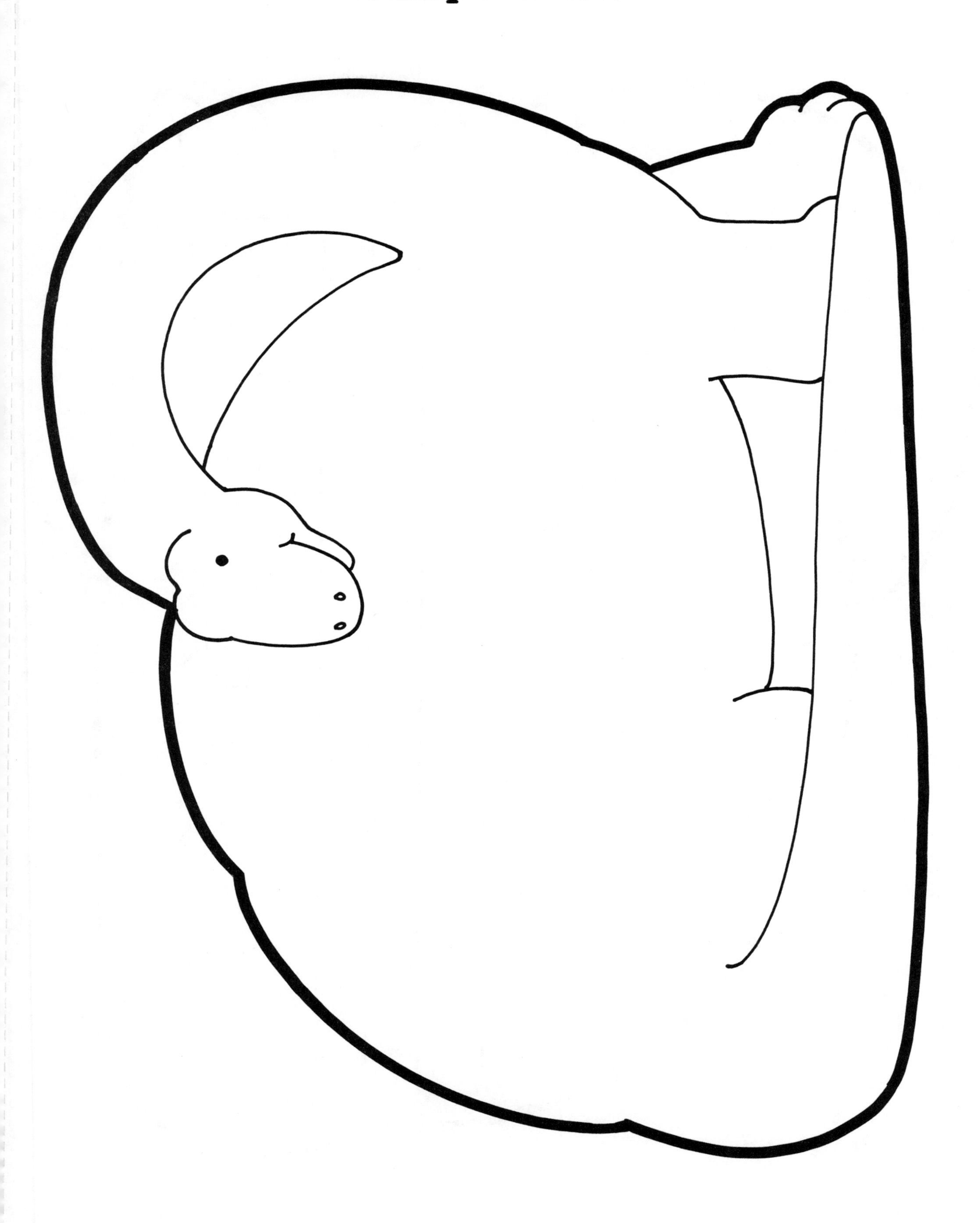

Shape Book

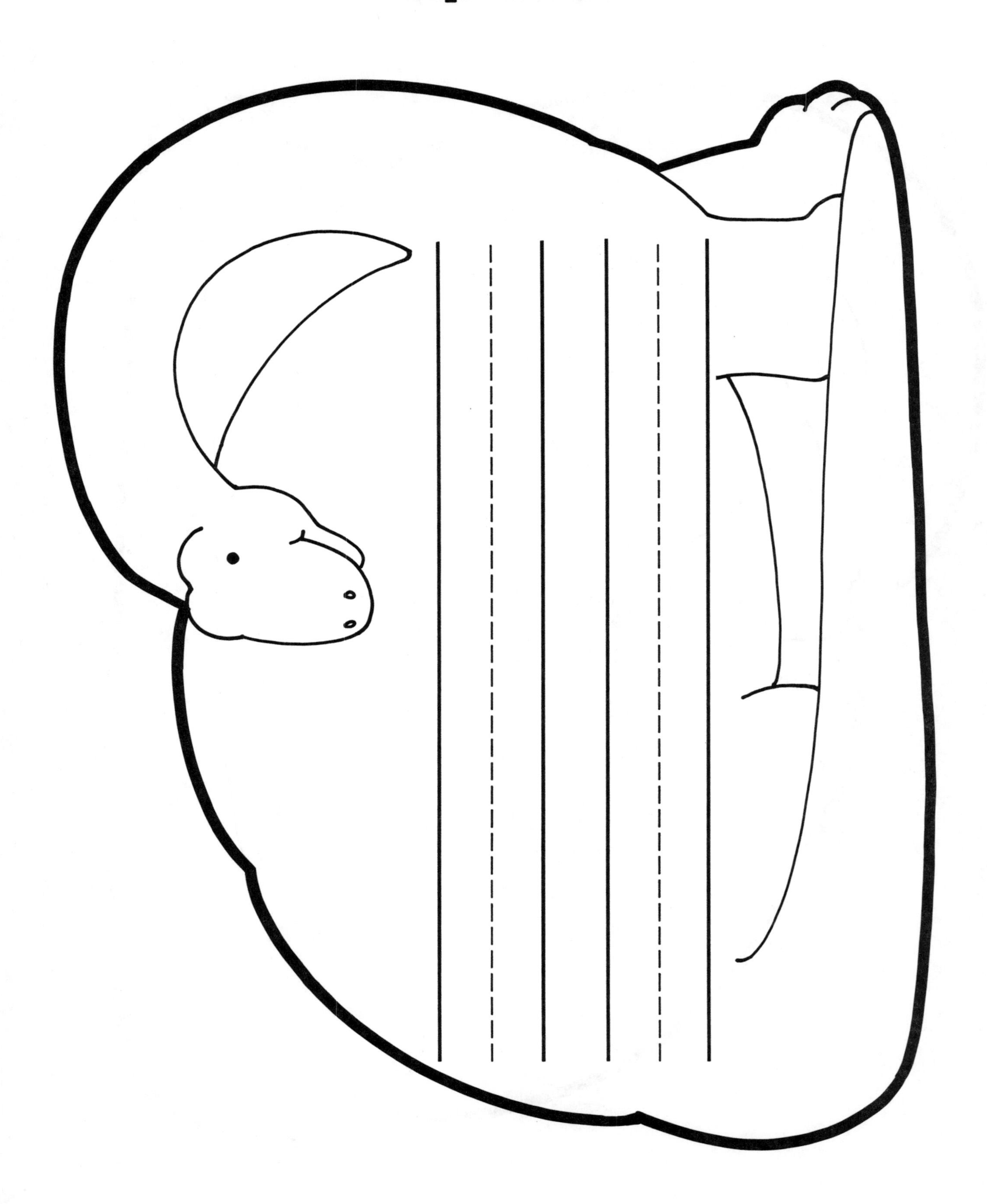

Theater

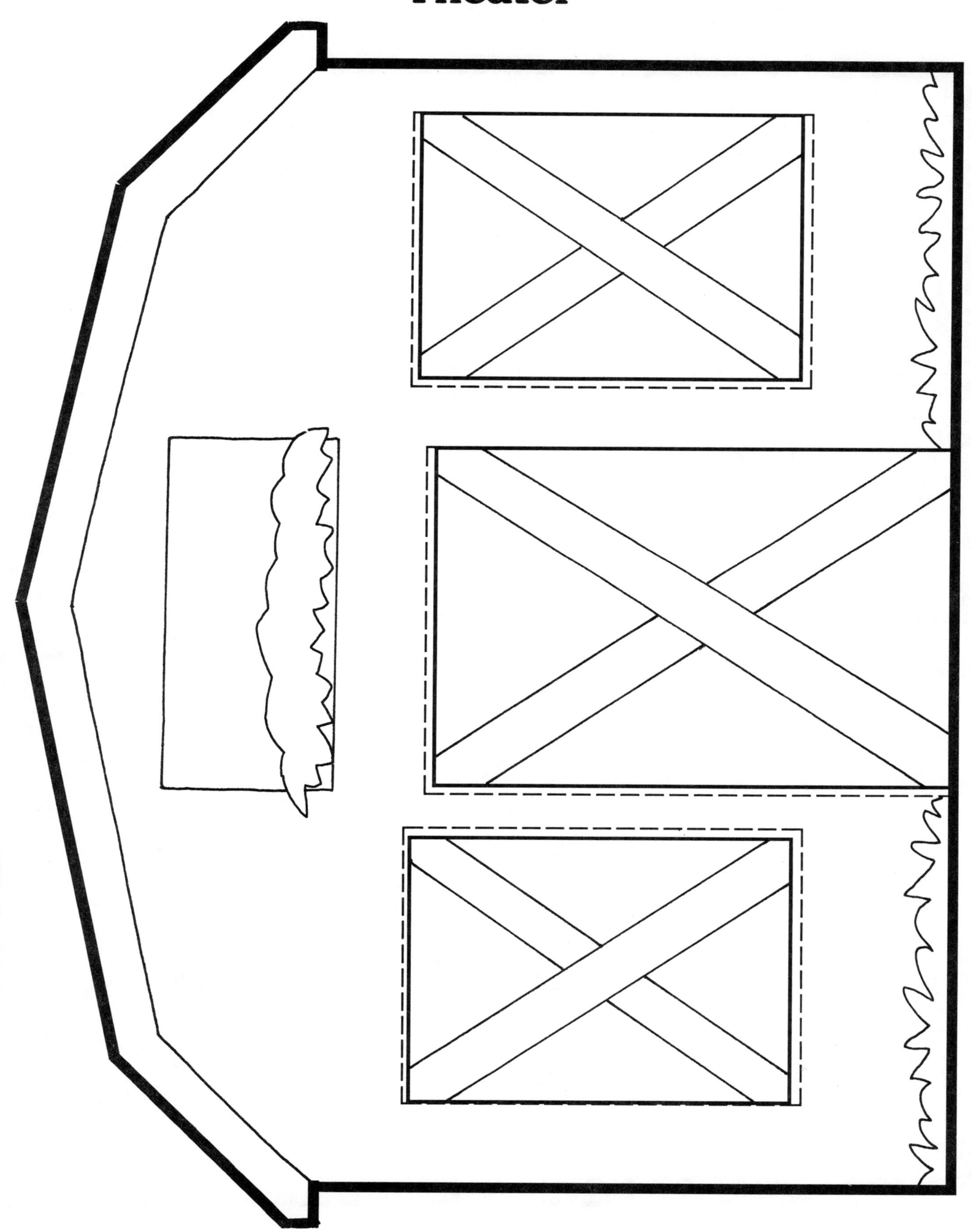

Theater

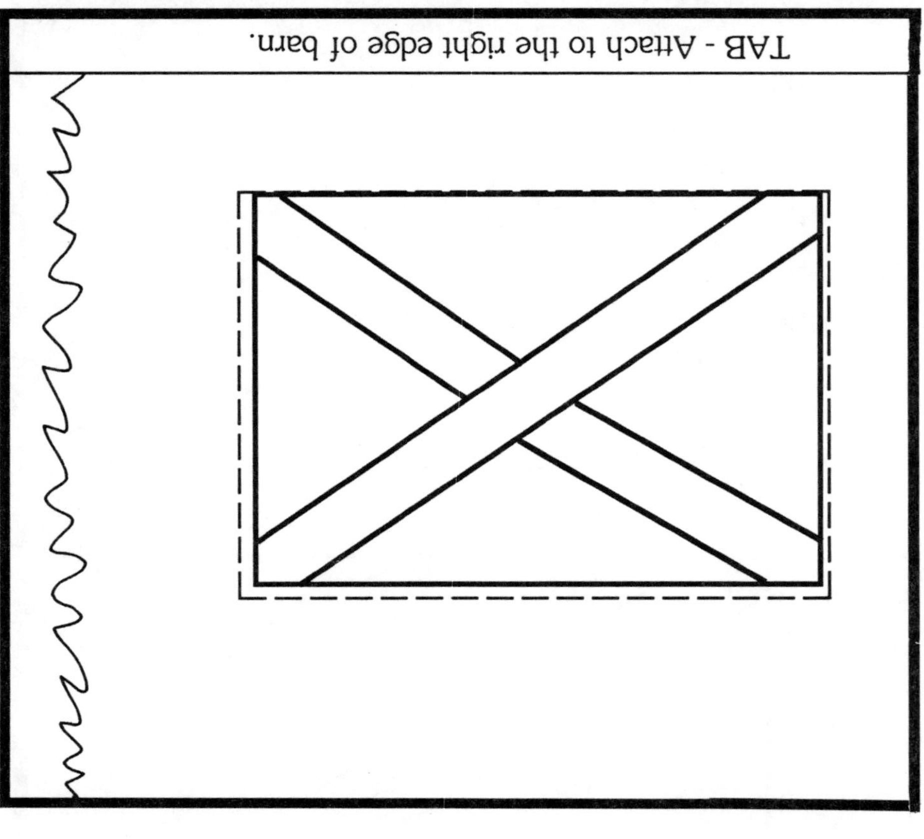
TAB - Attach to the right edge of barn.

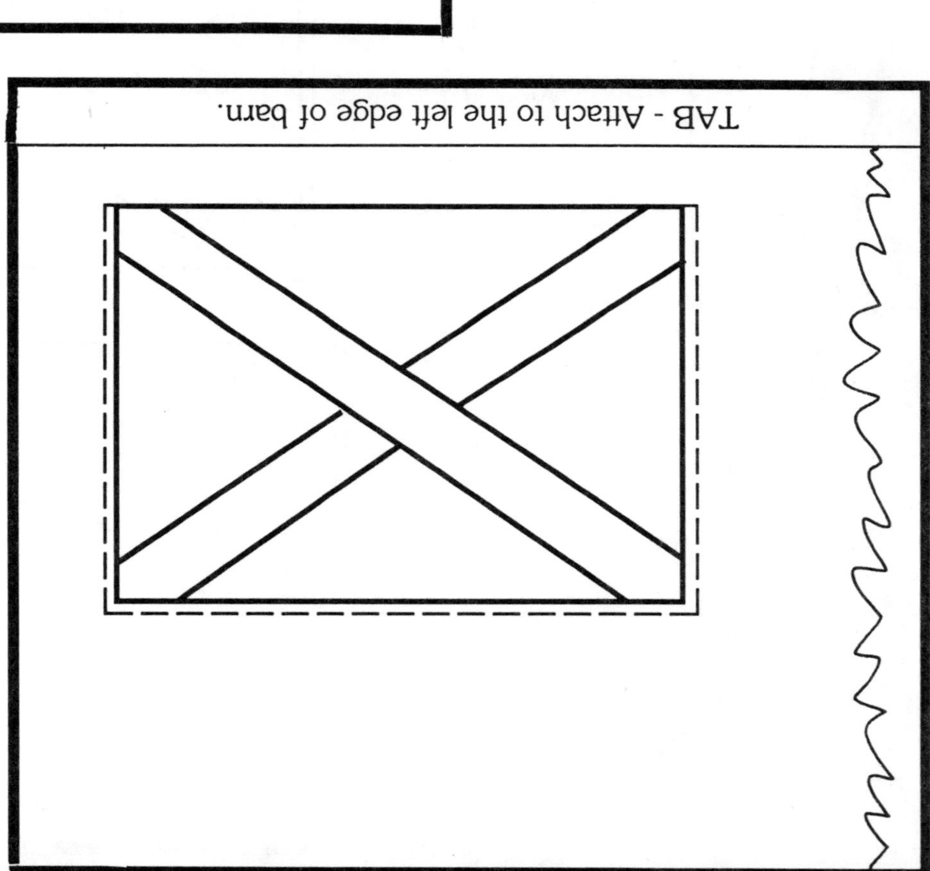
TAB - Attach to the left edge of barn.

Stick Puppets

Triceratops

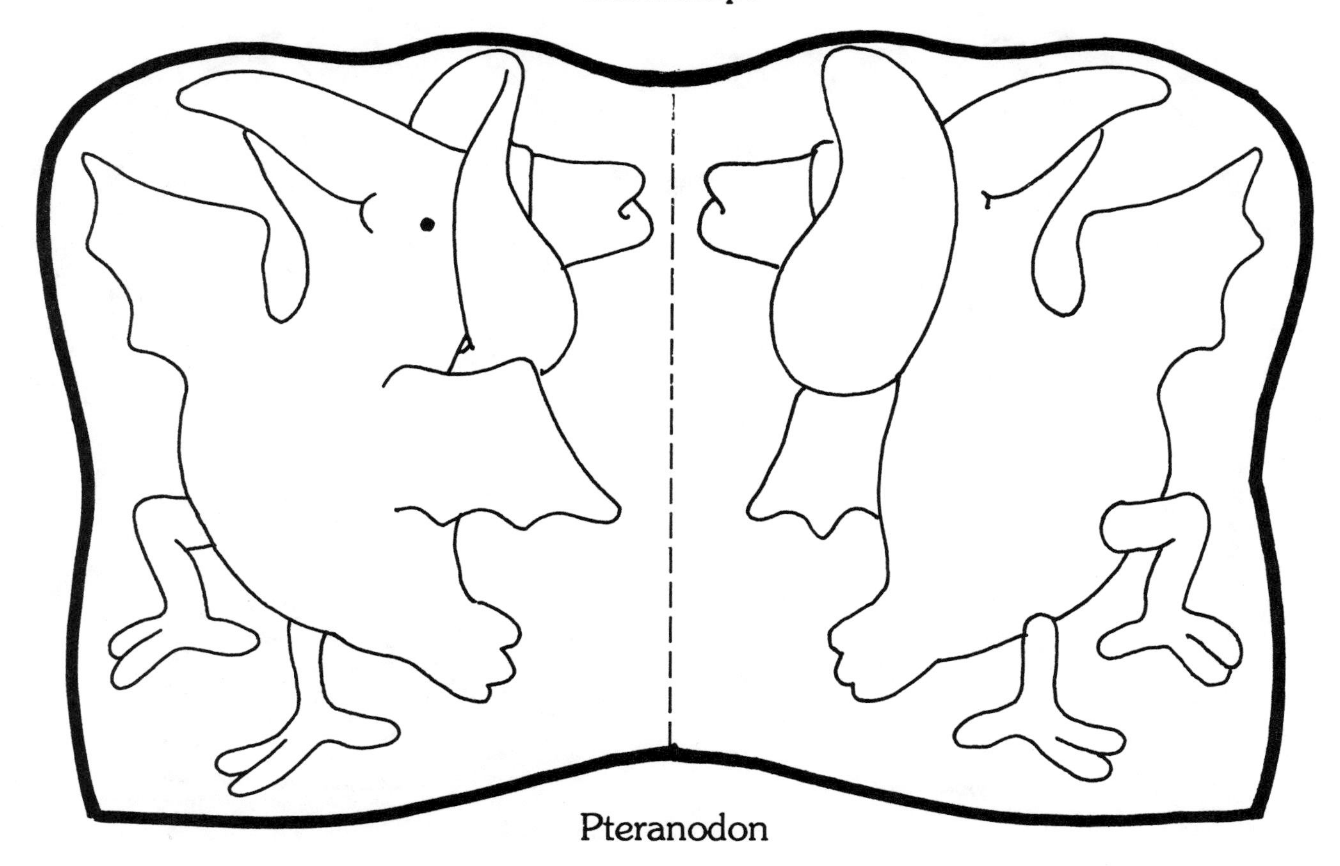

Pteranodon

Stick Puppets

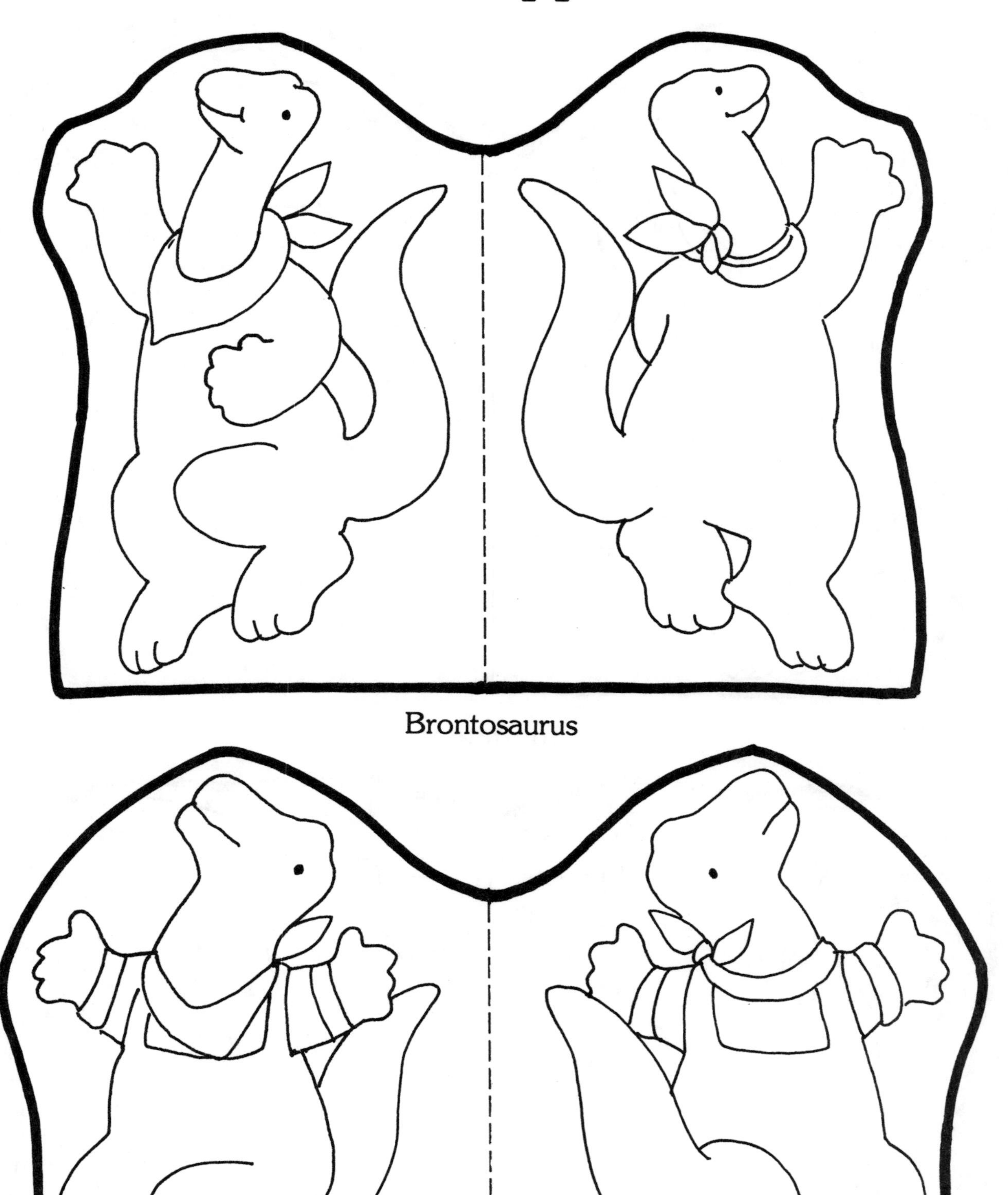

Brontosaurus

Tyrannosaurus Rex

Finger Puppets

Name ______________________________ **Open Worksheet**

Dinosaur Beenies

Name ______________________________ **Open Worksheet**

Dinosaur Doughnuts

Name ____________

Habitat - Egg

Baby Dinosaurs

Dr. Dinosaur's Body Chart

Dr. Dinosaur's Body Parts

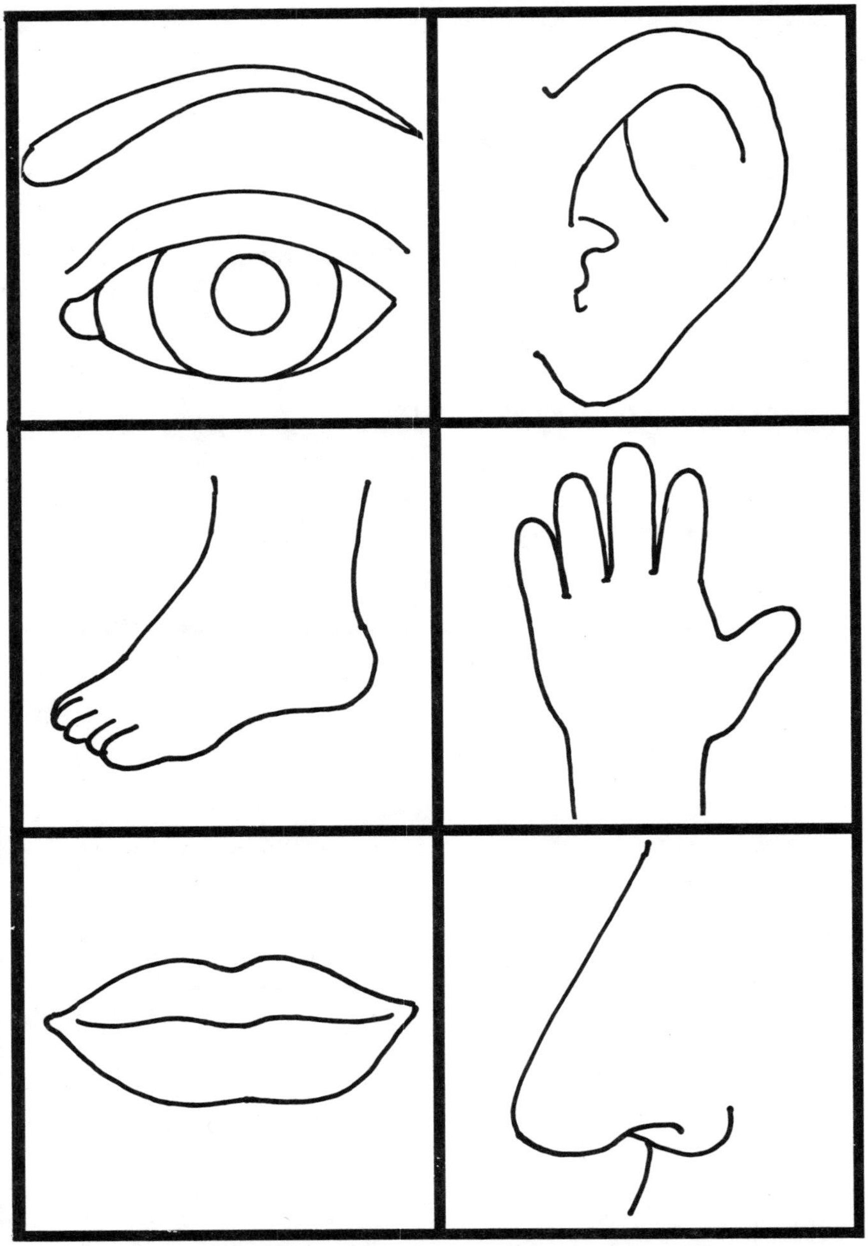

eye	ear	foot
hand	mouth	nose

Counter Dinosaurs

Dinner for Two Center

Dinner For Two Center

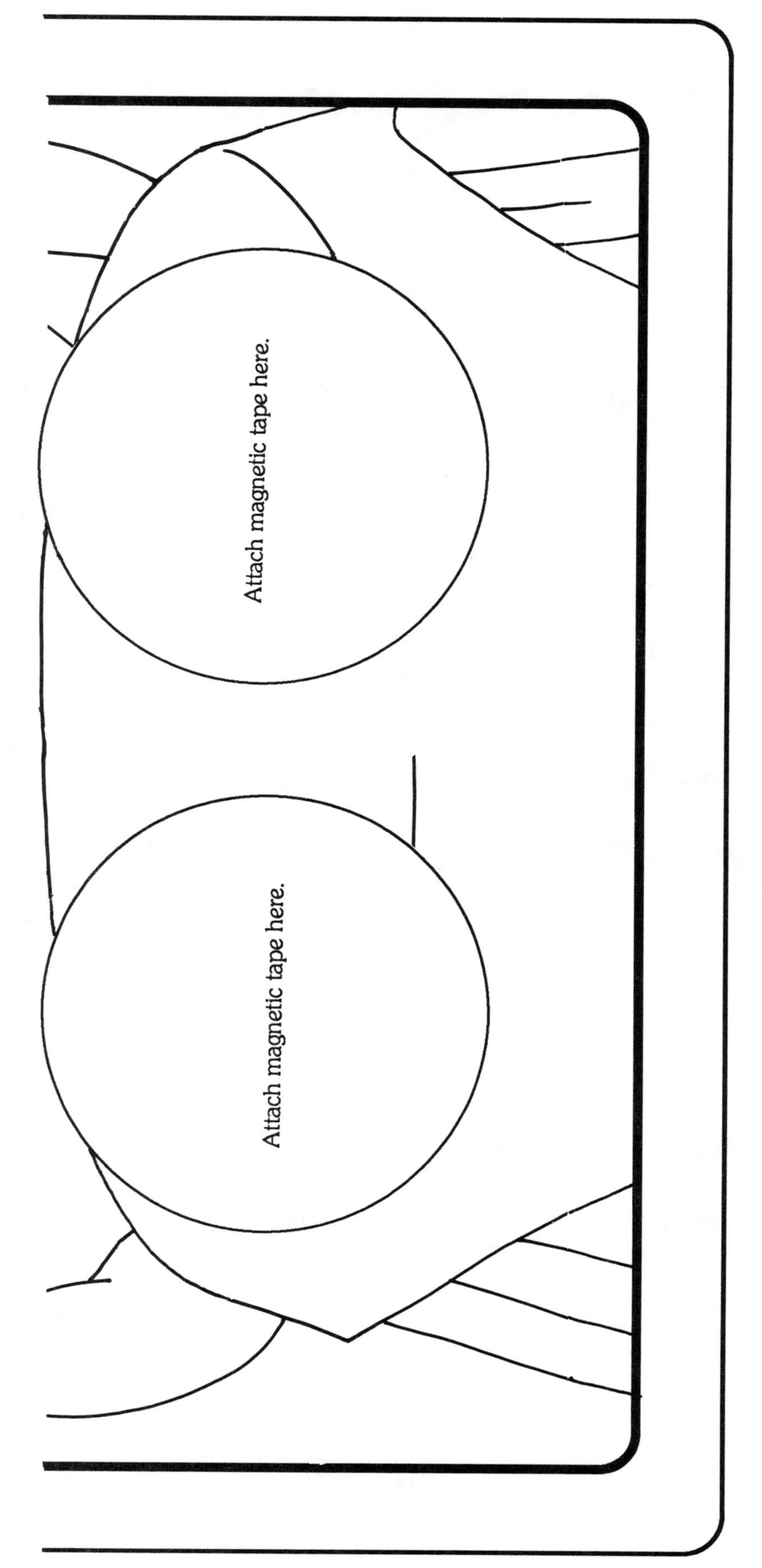

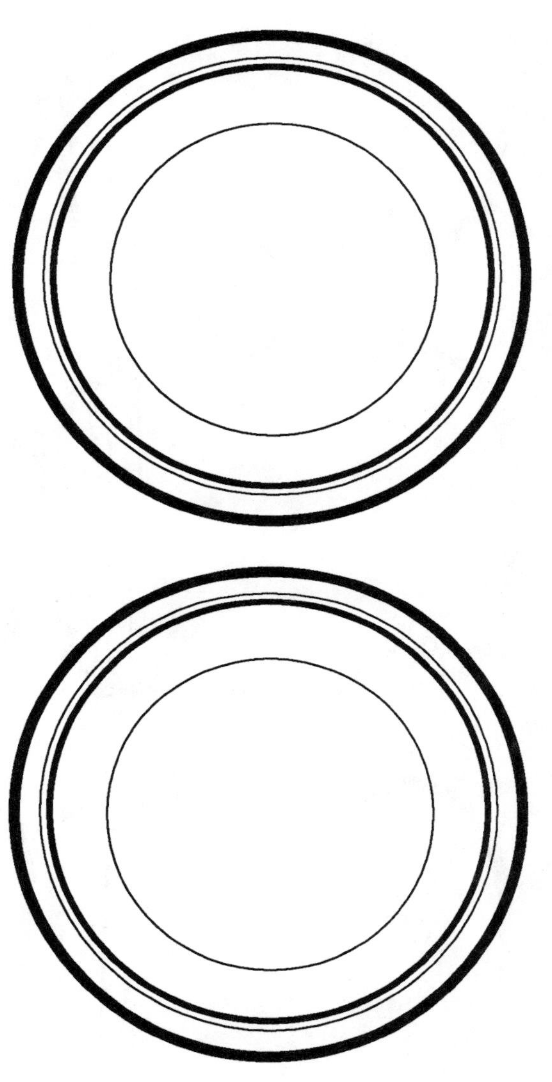

Sandwiches

Dinosaur Money

Land

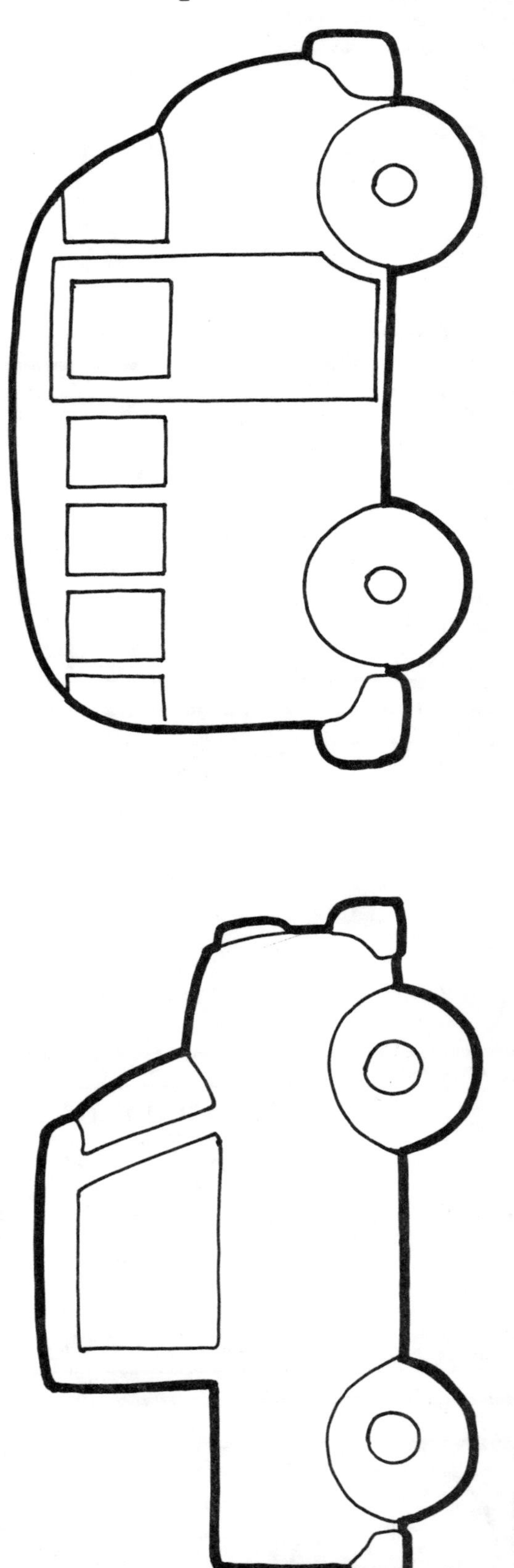

Water

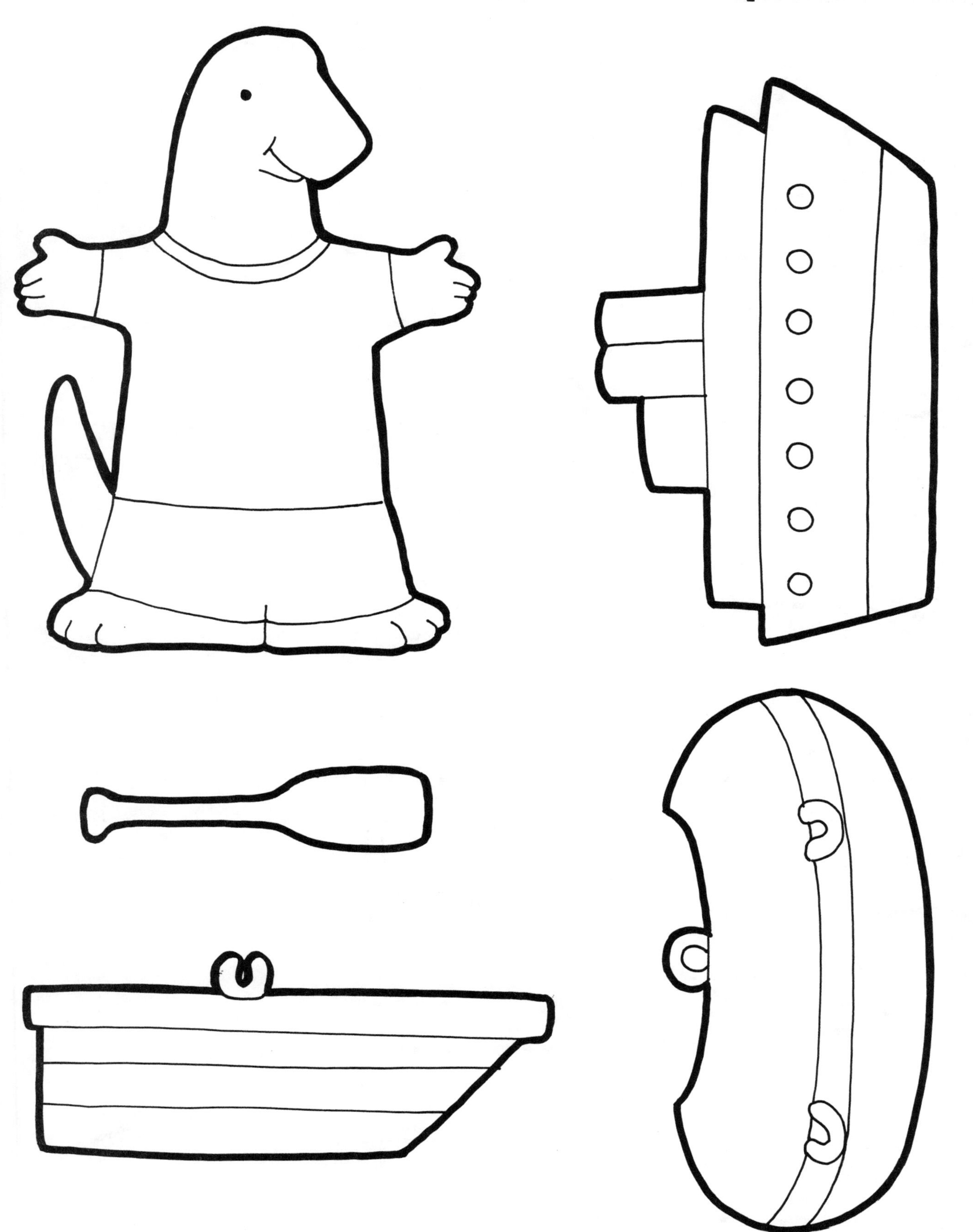

Play

Police Dinosaur

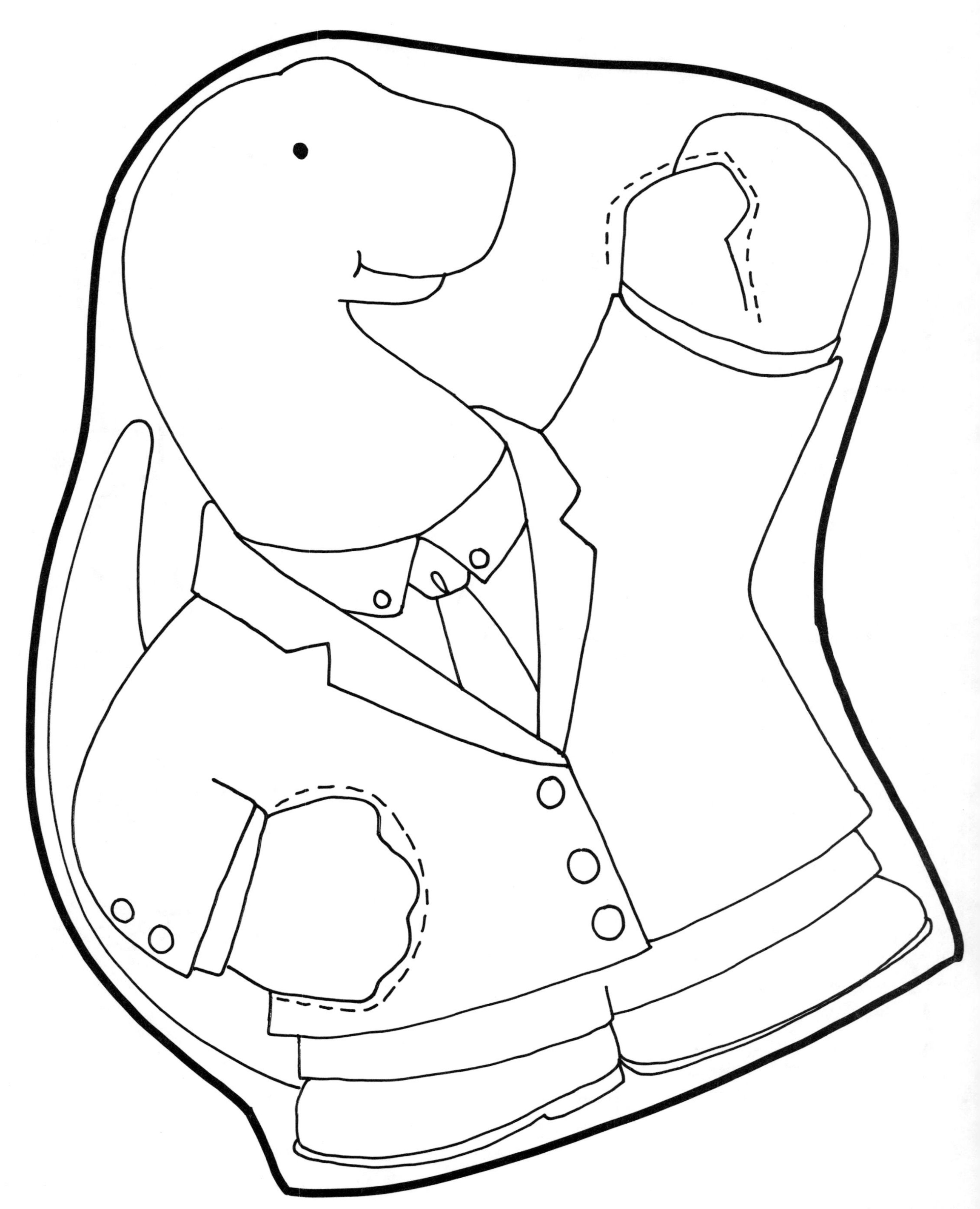

Police Dinosaur's Tools

Doctor Dinosaur

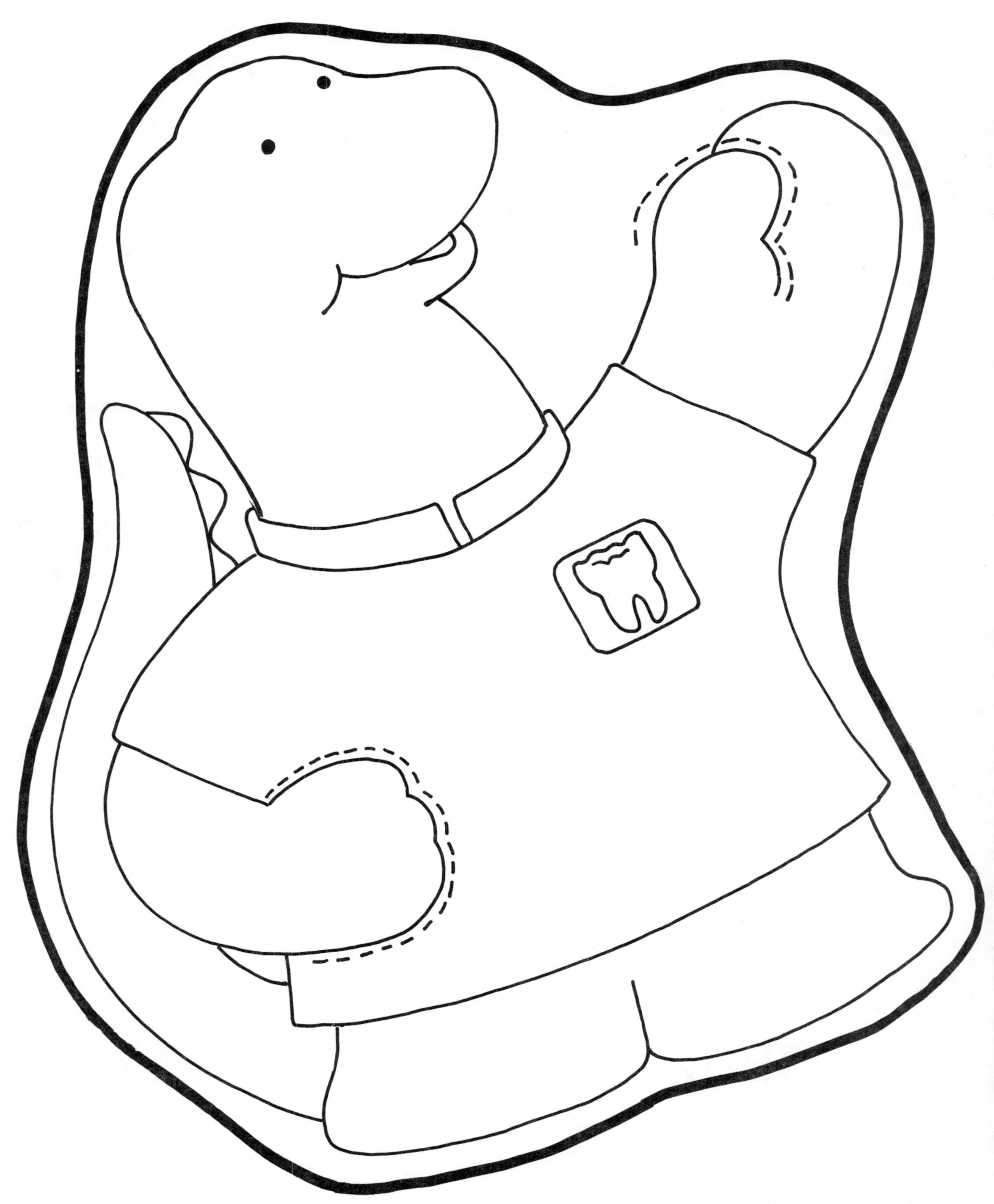

Doctor Dinosaur's Tools

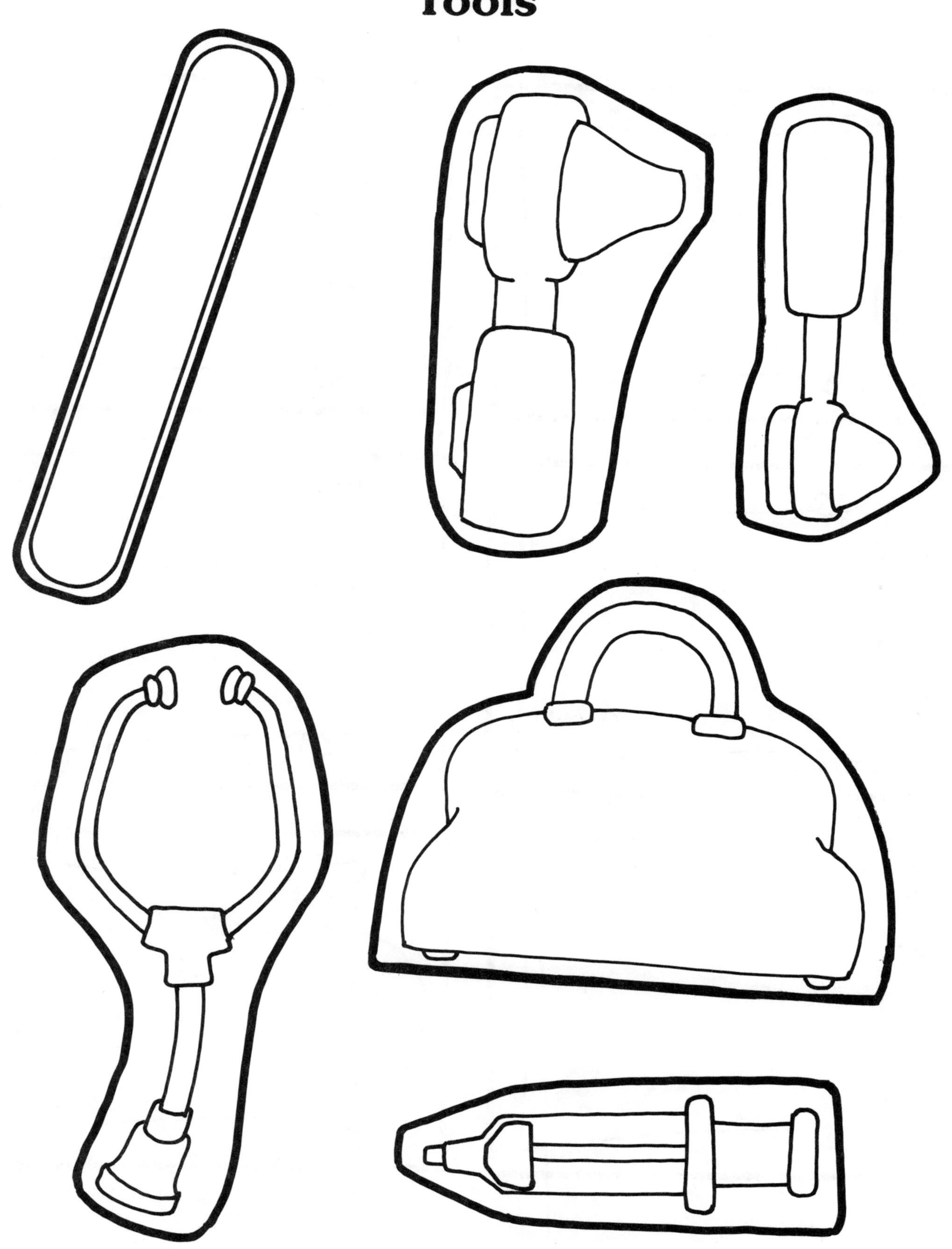

Dinosaur Flash Cards

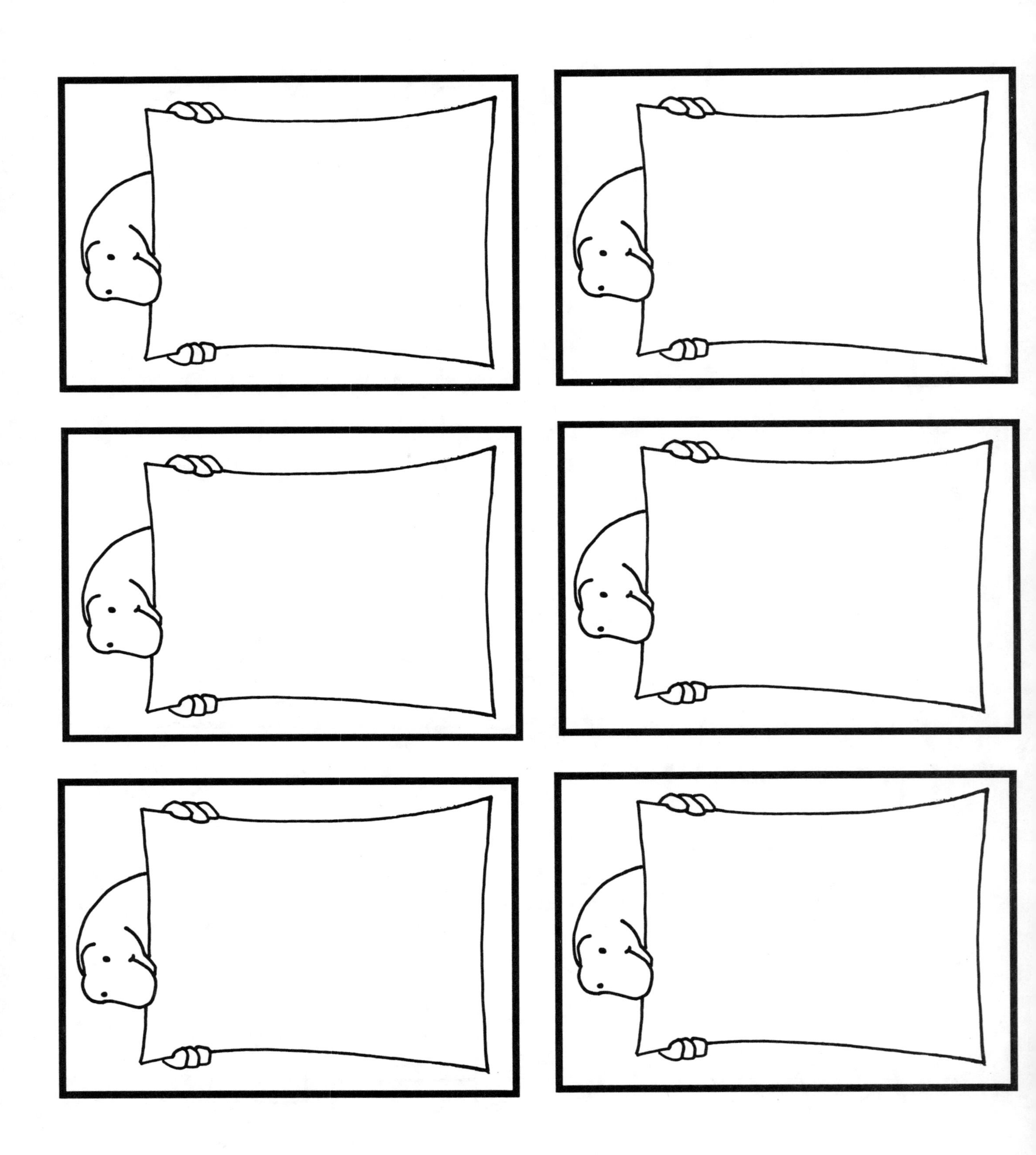

Dinosaur Flash Cards

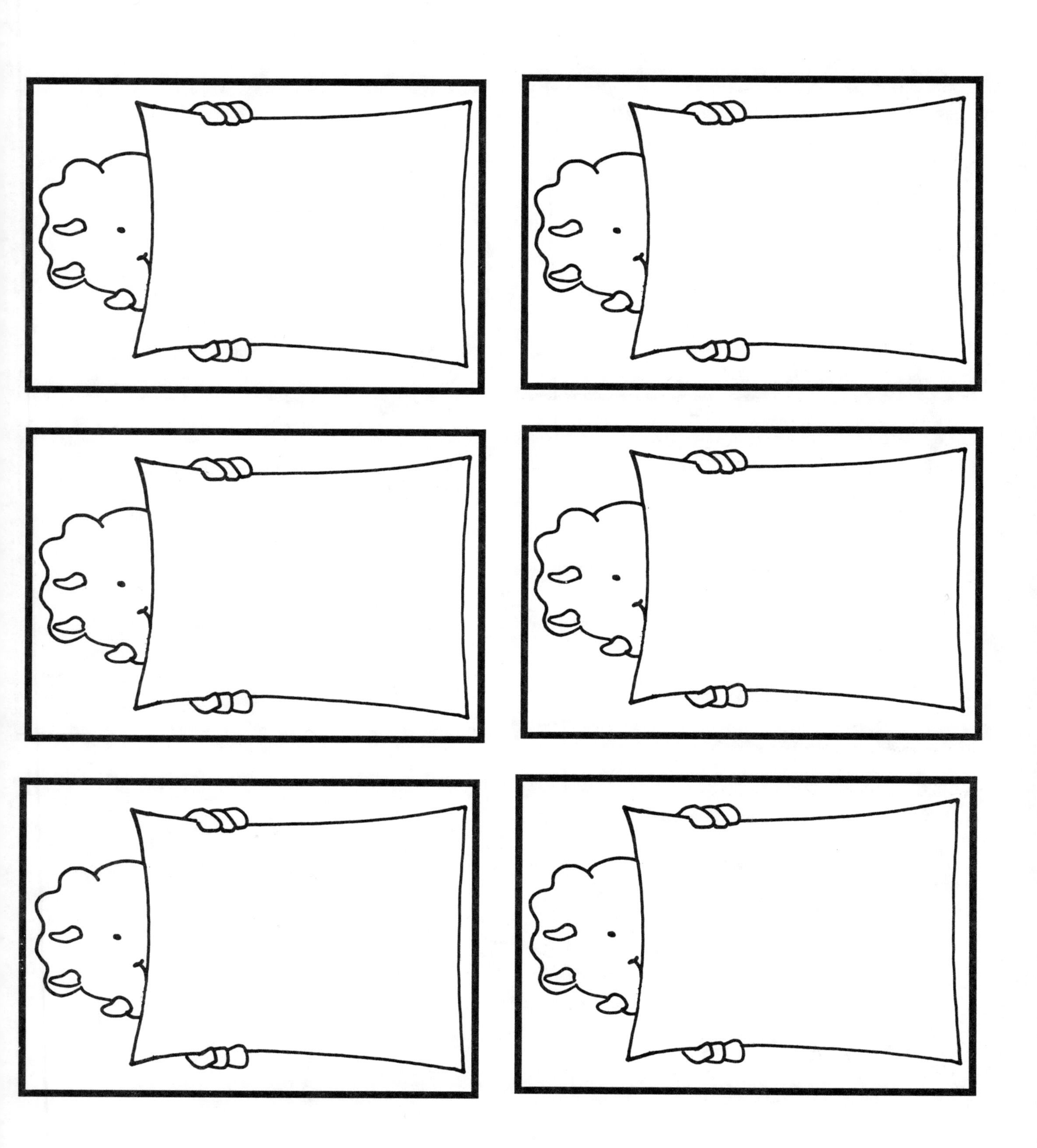

Dinosaur Pockets

Dinosaur Pockets

Dinosaur

SUNDAY	MONDAY	TUESDAY	WED

Calendar

EDNESDAY	THURSDAY	FRIDAY	SATURDAY

Gameboard

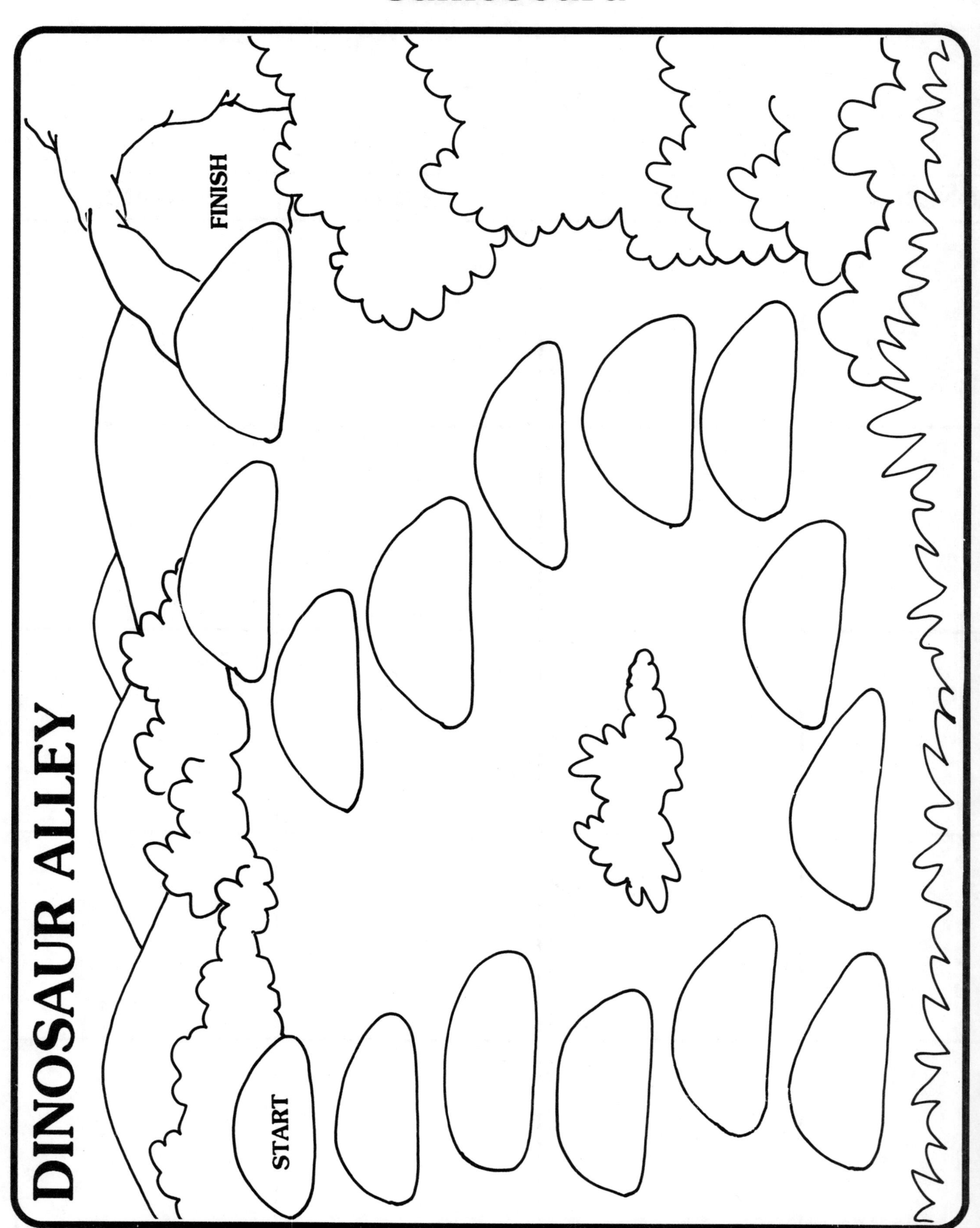

Pawns and Spinner

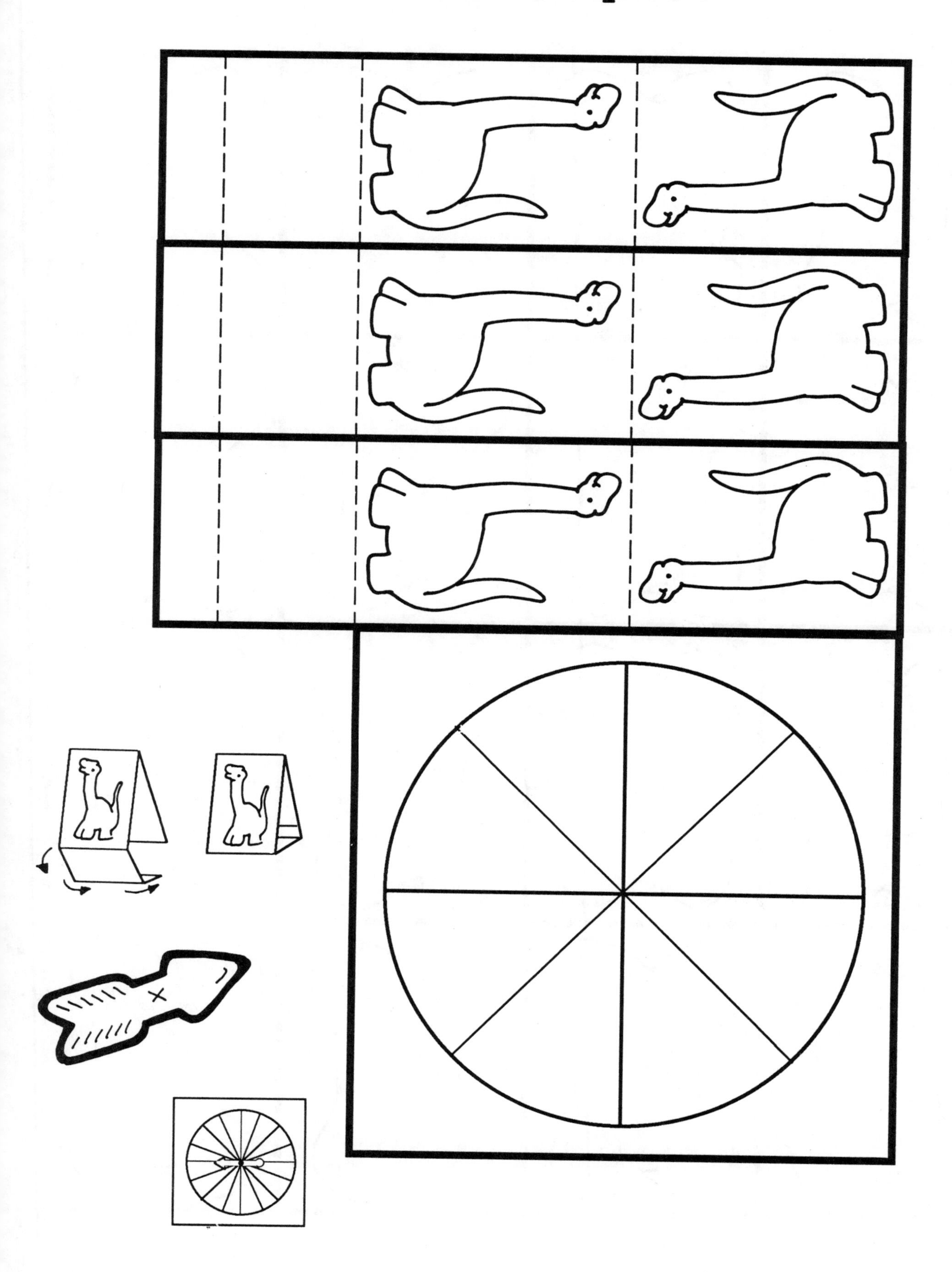

Bone Cards

Party Patterns

Party Hat

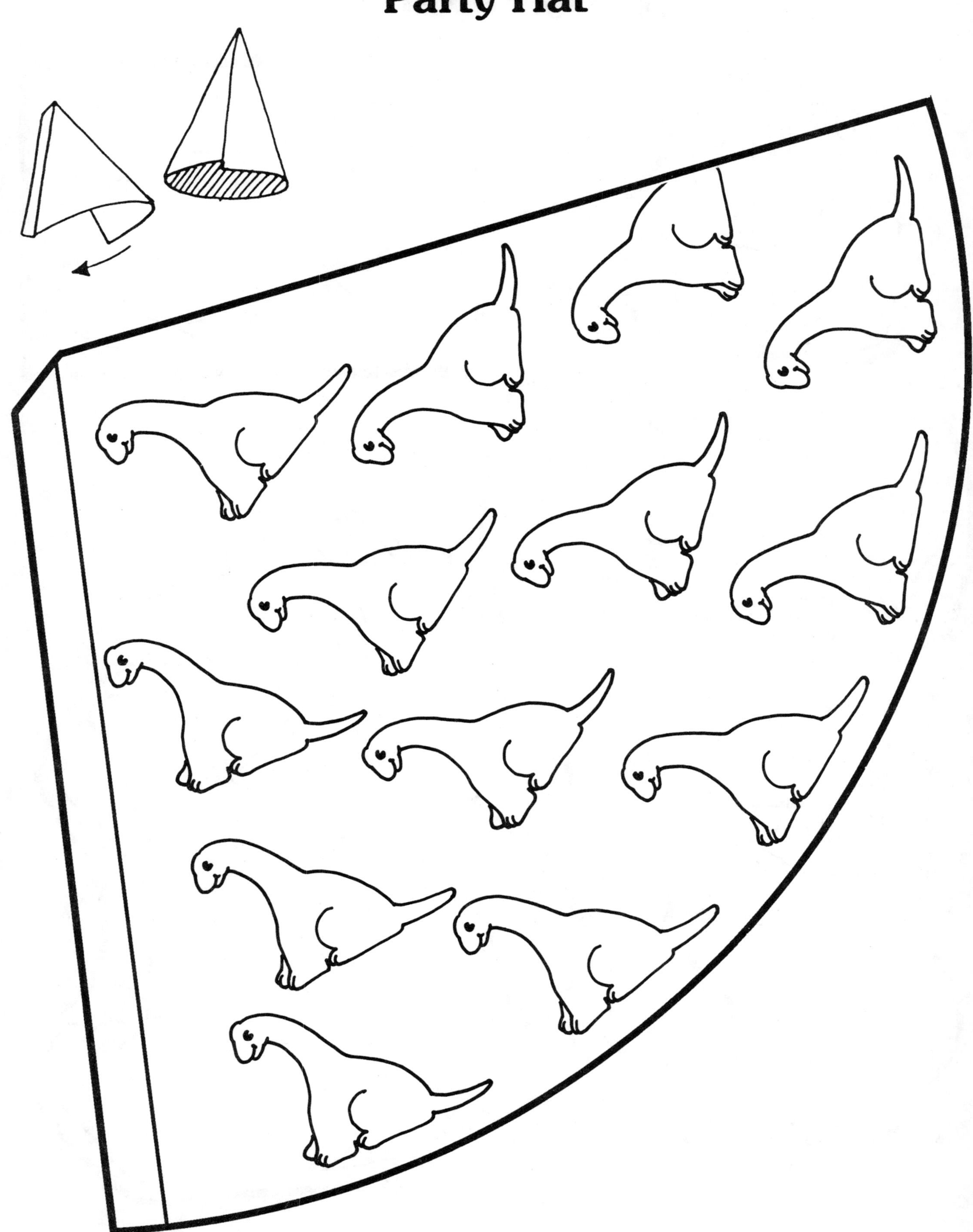